Flynn and the Bubble Gum Balloon

©Published 2022.
BookLife Publishing Ltd.
King's Lynn, Norfolk PE30 4LS

ISBN 978-1-80155-166-3

Flynn and the Bubble Gum Balloon
Written by A H Benjamin, Adapted by Robin Twiddy
Illustrated by Marcus Gray

An Introduction to Accessible Readers...

Our 'really readable' Accessible Readers have been specifically created to support the reading development of young readers with learning differences, such as dyslexia.

Our aim is to share our love of books with children, providing the same learning and developmental opportunities to every child.

INCREASED FONT SIZE AND SPACING improves readability and ensures text feels much less crowded.

OFF-WHITE BACKGROUNDS ON MATTE PAPER improves text contrast and avoids dazzling readers.

SIMPLIFIED PAGE LAYOUT reduces distractions and aids concentration.

CAREFULLY CRAFTED along guidelines set out in the British Dyslexia Association's Dyslexia-Friendly Style Guide.

Flynn and the Bubble Gum Balloon

Written by A H Benjamin
Illustrated by Marcus Gray

Flynn loved bubble gum. He loved to feel it squish and stretch as he chewed. He always had a piece of gum, chewing pink circles in his mouth, round and round. Flynn loved to blow bubbles. Huge, round, pink spheres.

Flynn would try to blow his bubbles bigger and rounder each time.

"That's amazing!" said all his friends.

One day, Flynn entered a bubble-blowing show. He won first place! The prize was thirty thousand bubble gum swirls. They were sent to his house that day.

"These will last me until my birthday!" cried Flynn, excitedly.

At school, Flynn's pockets were bursting with bubble gum swirls. He shared them out.

"I'll blow a bubble so fat and round, it will lift me off the ground!" Flynn boasted.

Flynn threw even more bubble gum swirls into his mouth. Chomp! Chomp! Chomp! Flynn began to blow with all his might. He blew a round, pink bubble. As Flynn blew, the bubble grew bigger and bigger...

Everybody stared. Their eyes grew wider. Slowly, Flynn's feet lifted off the ground. He began to float upwards. Up and up towards the clouds...

Before anybody could do anything about it, Flynn and the giant bubble were drifting up, into the sky!

Flynn looked down. On the ground, his friends were tiny. His teacher, shouting up at him, was no bigger than a mouse.

At first he was scared, but soon he became used to the feeling of flying.

"This is cool!" he thought, excitedly.

Flynn drifted like a big, pink cloud, out of the town and over the trees.

Suddenly, a big, black bird flew out of the clouds towards him. The bird circled around the bubble.

"Oh, no!" Flynn thought. "If it bursts my bubble, I'll fall to the ground!"

He couldn't shout with the bubble in his mouth! How could he scare the bird away? Flynn had to do something.

He searched his pockets and found some things to throw at the bird. A bubble gum swirl... A pound coin... A shiny, brown conker...

But the stubborn bird wouldn't go away. It was flying closer and closer to Flynn's bubble.

Reaching deeper into his pockets, Flynn found his lucky silver marble. When it saw the marble, the bird forgot all about the bubble.

He held out his hand, hoping to lure the bird with the shiny toy. The bird swooped down and scooped the marble into its beak. It flew off, swirling down towards its nest in the trees below.

"Phew!" thought Flynn. The bubble was safe.

Flynn had not gone far when he saw a majestic, red dragon swooping above him. The dragon seemed to be attached to a string. Phew! It wasn't a real dragon, with its flaming red eyes and tail lashing about. It was a kite!

The dragon kite whirled towards the bubble. Whoosh! It only just missed. It twirled around the bubble again. Flynn tried to catch the dragon and grab its long tail as it whirled past. But he missed. He needed something he could bash the kite with.

With a bit of a struggle, Flynn reached down and took off one of his shoes. He held the laces firmly in his hand and swung the shoe round in a circle.

"This should do the trick," Flynn thought.

Just then, the dragon swirled towards him once more. Flynn knew he had to hit it with his first try. He mustn't hit the bubble!

Aiming carefully, he began to swing his shoe faster. It made a whooshing sound.

He let go – just as the kite came closer to him. The shoe shot through the air and then...

CRASH!

It struck the dragon, which fell through the clouds towards the ground, with the shoe following close behind it.

"Whoopeee!" Flynn felt like shrieking.

Flynn was soaring over the countryside. Everything looked small and far away. Beneath him he could see the leafy tops of the silver birch trees around the park.

A circus was arriving. Their wagons, painted all different colours, looked like toys.

It all looked so strange that Flynn hardly noticed until it was too late.

A huge group of hot air balloons had appeared all around him! There were at least thirty giant, round balloons! He was surrounded.

The balloons were everywhere. Flynn's feet hit a balloon. Without thinking, he crouched and pushed... And bounced off and away! Flynn bounced and jumped from balloon to balloon. He bounced up and down and all around until his head was dizzy.

Suddenly, Flynn's shoelace caught on the skirt of the biggest balloon. It had wound around the ropes and was dragging Flynn with it!

"Ouch!" thought Flynn. "My foot!"

He didn't want to be dragged away. Flynn spun twice in the air.

He squirmed about and managed to kick his shoe with his other foot until it fell off. He was free! Flynn floated upwards towards the clouds.

"That was close," Flynn thought, closing his mouth firmly around the gum.

Flynn thought he might like to get back to the ground soon. He spotted three dots in the distance.

"Now what?" Flynn wondered, nervously.

A team of three jet fighters flew towards him, with streams of red, blue and orange smoke trailing behind them.

"I need to get out of here!" thought Flynn, as the bubble spun again.

The jets roared past Flynn. Both he and the bubble twisted in the air. He wanted to yell "look out!" but the bubble would have fallen out of his mouth.

The noise died away and the planes vanished in a great cloud of swirling colours.

The bubble was dirty with red, blue and orange smoke. Was that a little hole there? Sure enough, the bubble was losing air. Slowly, Flynn floated towards the ground.

Flynn was flying low over the town. People began to notice him. They stared and pointed. Flynn skimmed over treetops and weaved between the roofs of houses.

"I will never blow a bubble as big as this again," Flynn promised himself.

He looked all around. He could see his house! The first one on the street. Flynn's mum was hanging the washing out. He landed softly next to the birdbath.

"Hi, Mum," said Flynn chirpily.

The bubble ran out of air at last. It drooped down over Flynn, covering him from head to toe. Startled, Flynn's mum spun around. She screamed, then rushed into the house.

"Oh dear," sighed Flynn. "I guess I have a lot of explaining to do!"

Flynn and the Bubble Gum Balloon: Quiz

1. How many bubble gum swirls did Flynn win?

2. What do you think Flynn's teacher was shouting up at him?

3. What did Flynn hit the dragon kite with?

4. What did Flynn's shoelace get caught on?

5. How do you think Flynn felt when he was floating in the sky? How do you think you would feel?

Helpful Hints for Reading at Home

This 'really readable' Accessible Reader has been carefully written and designed to help children with learning differences whether they are reading in the classroom or at home. However, there are some extra ways in which you can help your child at home.

- Try to provide a quiet space for your child to read, with as few distractions as possible.

- Try to allow your child as much time as they need to decode the letters and words on the page.

- Reading with a learning difference can be frustrating and difficult. Try to let your child take short, managed breaks between reading sessions if they begin to feel frustrated.

- Build your child's confidence with positive praise and encouragement throughout.

- Your child's teacher, as well as many charities, can provide you with lots of tips and techniques to help your child read at home.